ED SUETA

RECORDER METHOD

Dear Recorder Student,

Congratulations on your choice to learn to play the recorder!

Learning to play the recorder will be an enjoyable experience. By playing the songs, duets and rhythm charts in my book, you will develop the important skills needed to become a great musician!

I hope you will enjoy this book and enjoy using the Play-Along Tapes or CD.

Music will bring you fun and enjoyment throughout your life!

Musically yours,

Ed Sueta

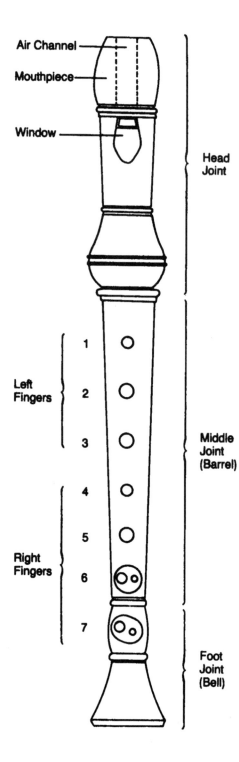

Air Channel

Mouthpiece

Window

Head Joint

Left Fingers — 1 2 3

Middle Joint (Barrel)

Right Fingers — 4 5 6 7

Foot Joint (Bell)

HOW TO PLAY THE RECORDER

Left Hand

The left hand is placed at the top of the recorder. The left thumb covers the hole underneath the recorder. The 1st finger covers the first hole, the 2nd finger covers the 2nd hole and the 3rd finger covers the 3rd hole. The little finger of the left hand is not used. Cover all the holes with the balls of the fingers, not with the finger tips. The fingers should be slightly curved or flat.

Right Hand

The right hand is placed at the bottom of the recorder. The 1st finger covers the 4th hole, the 2nd finger covers the 5th hole, the 3rd finger covers the 6th hole and the little finger covers the 7th hole. The right thumb supports the recorder form underneath and should be placed beneath the 4th and 5th holes from the top. The right hand fingers should also be slightly curved or flat.

Playing Position

Hold the recorder in front of you at about a 45 degree angle, with your elbows slightly away from your body.

Lips

Place the mouthpiece on your lower lip and bring your upper lip down on top of the mouthpiece. No more than a 1/2 inch of the mouthpiece should be in your mouth, and your teeth and tongue should never touch the mouthpiece.

Tongue and Air

Start the tone by whispering into the mouthpiece. Your teacher will tell you what syllable to use. This is called tonguing. Your lips and jaw should not move when tonguing.

Care of Your Recorder

After playing, dry out the inside of your recorder with a lint free cloth (swab). The mouthpiece can be kept clean by washing it in warm, soapy water, then rinsing it in clear, warm water.

READING MUSIC

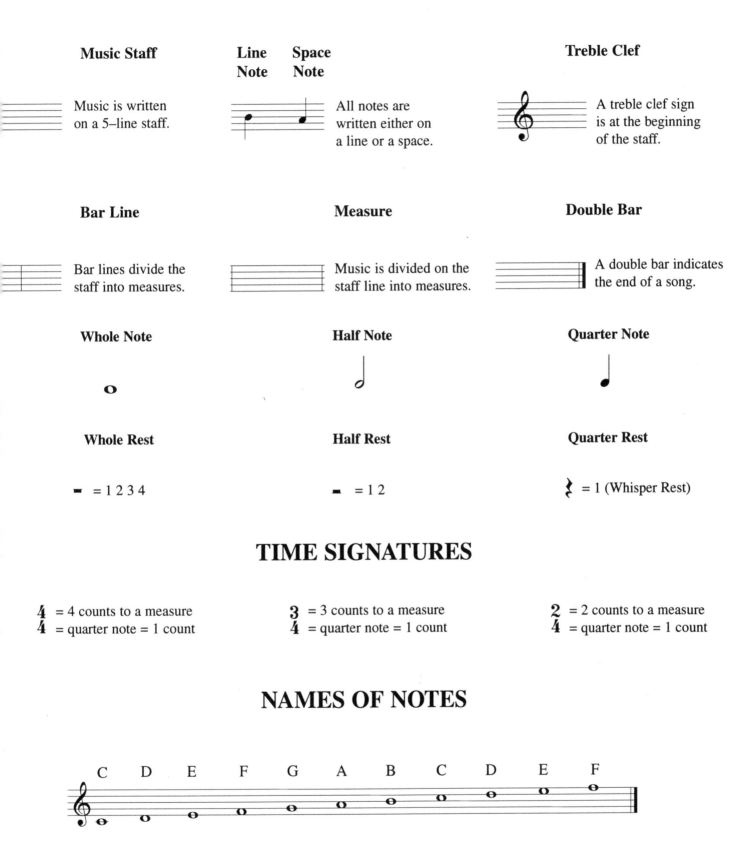

Music Staff

Music is written on a 5-line staff.

Line Note **Space Note**

All notes are written either on a line or a space.

Treble Clef

A treble clef sign is at the beginning of the staff.

Bar Line

Bar lines divide the staff into measures.

Measure

Music is divided on the staff line into measures.

Double Bar

A double bar indicates the end of a song.

Whole Note

Half Note

Quarter Note

Whole Rest

= 1 2 3 4

Half Rest

= 1 2

Quarter Rest

= 1 (Whisper Rest)

TIME SIGNATURES

$\frac{4}{4}$ = 4 counts to a measure
= quarter note = 1 count

$\frac{3}{4}$ = 3 counts to a measure
= quarter note = 1 count

$\frac{2}{4}$ = 2 counts to a measure
= quarter note = 1 count

NAMES OF NOTES

C D E F G A B C D E F

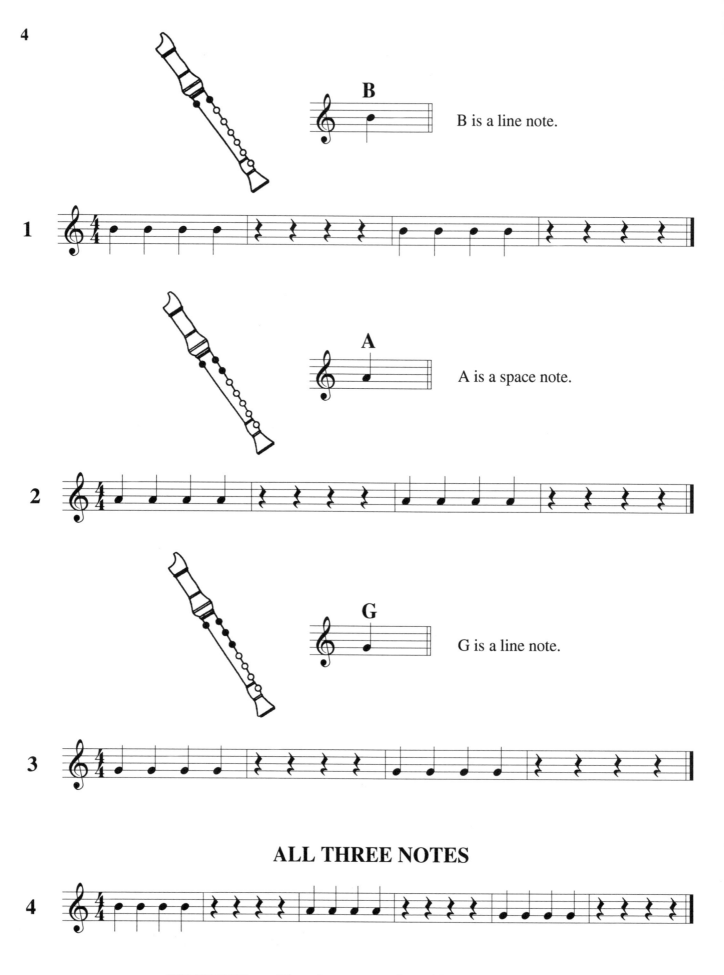

B is a line note.

A is a space note.

G is a line note.

ALL THREE NOTES

REMEMBER: All music notes are written either on a line or a space.

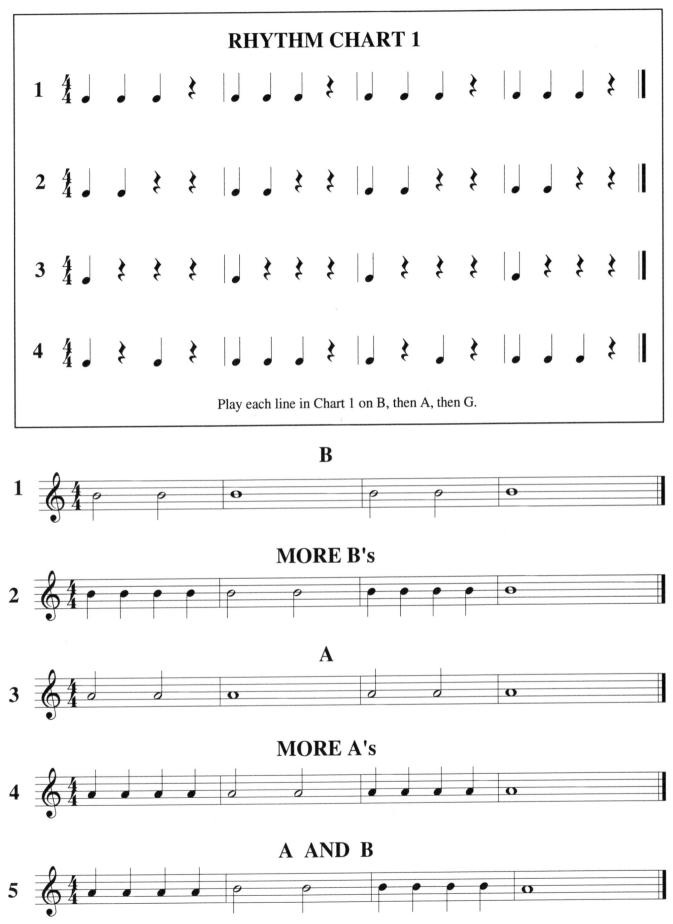

G

MORE G's

B A G

AIR CONTROL

Write in seconds.

How many seconds can you hold B, A and G?

Breathe deeply before starting each note.

Blow smooth and gentle air.

HOT CROSS BUNS

English

Hot   cross   buns,   hot   cross   buns.

Repeat from beginning

One   a   pen - ny,   two   a   pen - ny,   hot   cross   buns.

RHYTHM CHART 2

' = Breath mark*

Play each line in Chart 2 on G, A and B. - Not too fast!

*Try to play 2 measures in 1 breath.

FRENCH SONG

Traditional

CHALLENGE LINE

Repeat several times for smooth fingers.

MERRILY WE ROLL ALONG

Traditional

Mer - ri - ly we roll a - long, roll a - long, roll a - long.

Mer - ri - ly we roll a - long, O'er the deep blue sea.

THREE LINES FOR SMOOTH FINGERS

Repeat lines 1,2 and 3 several times.

LULLABY

Slowly

Welsh

p = Softly

OUR FIRST DUET

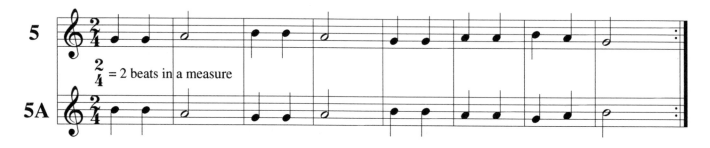

FOLK SONG-ADAPTED

Estonian

ROCKIN'

Ed Sueta

POLKA DOT POLKA

Ed Sueta

AIR CONTROL

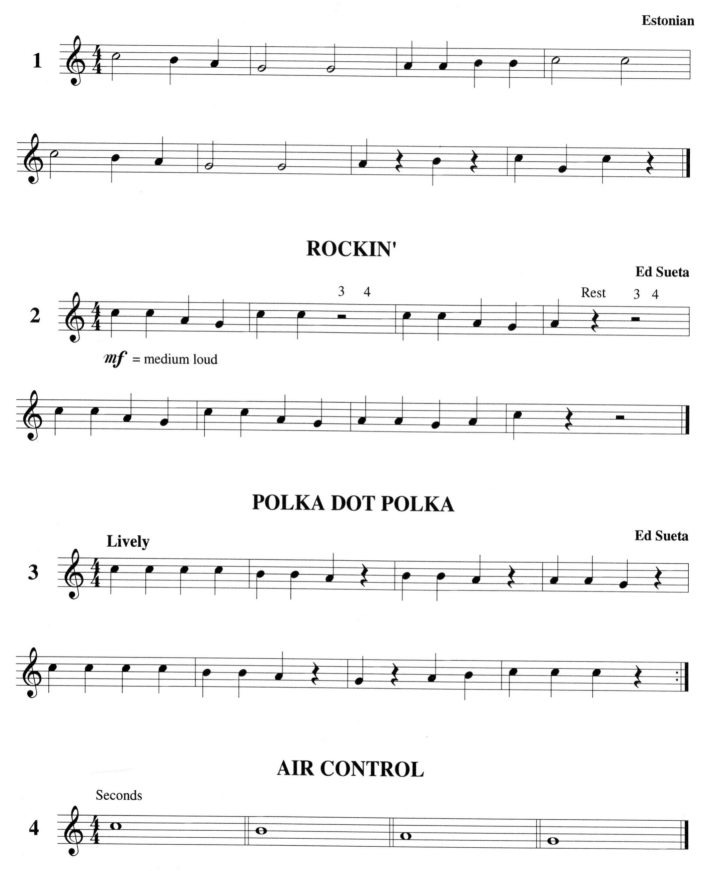

FRENCH TUNE

Traditional

AIR TEST

1 2 3 4 5 6 7 8 9 10 11 12 13 14 15 16

⌣ = Tie - Tongue the first note only, continue to blow steady air.
How far can you go in one breath? Circle the highest number you reach.

FOR FINGER CONTROL

Repeat several times.

JINGLE BELLS

Pierpont

mf Jin - gle Bells! Jin - gle Bells! Jin - gle all the way!

Oh what fun it is to ride in a one horse o - pen sle - igh!

Jin - gle Bells! Jin - gle Bells! Jin - gle all the way!

Oh what fun it is to ride in a one horse o - pen sleigh!

RHYTHM CHART 3

Play each line in Chart 3 on all the notes you know.

THE BARCAROLLE
Offenbach

GERMAN WALTZ
Traditional

FOR SMOOTH FINGERS

LIGHTLY ROW

FAIS DO DO

Repeat several times.

Light - ly row, light - ly row, o'er the glas - sy waves we go.

Smooth - ly glide, smooth - ly glide, on the si - lent tide.

Let the wind and wa - ters be, min - gled with our mel - o - dy.

Sing and float, sing and float, in our lit - tle boat.

French

mp = medium soft

Fine

Go back to beginning
and play to Fine. ——→ **D.C. al Fine**

RHYTHM CHART 4

HOT CROSS BUNS

English

PARTY SONG - ADAPTED

U.S.A.

MARY HAD A LITTLE LAMB

Ma - ry had a lit - tle lamb, lit - tle lamb, lit - tle lamb.

Ma - ry had a lit - tle lamb, it's fleece was white as snow.

TWO STEP MARCH

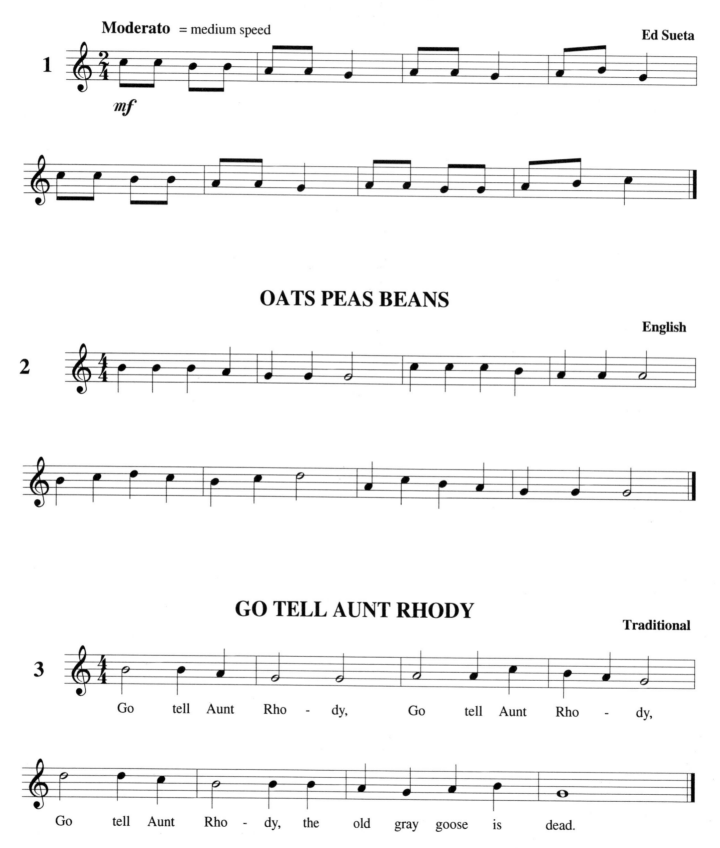

OATS PEAS BEANS

GO TELL AUNT RHODY

Go tell Aunt Rho - dy, Go tell Aunt Rho - dy,

Go tell Aunt Rho - dy, the old gray goose is dead.

REST TEST

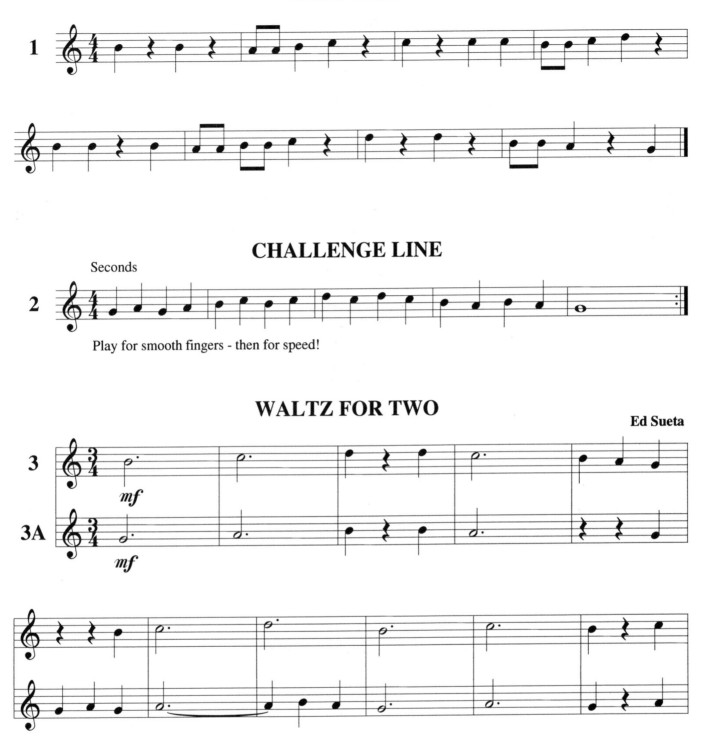

CHALLENGE LINE

Seconds

Play for smooth fingers - then for speed!

WALTZ FOR TWO

Ed Sueta

FRENCH FOLK SONG

Traditional

Pick-up notes - Notes before the first complete
measure are called pick-up notes.

FOLK TUNE

Italian

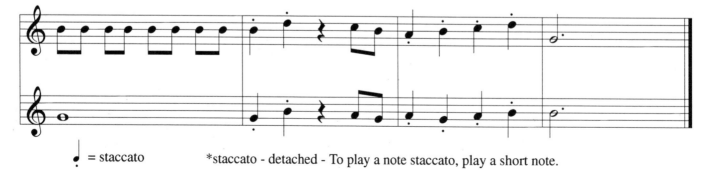

♩ = staccato   *staccato - detached - To play a note staccato, play a short note.

20

E

E is a line note.

ALL E's

1

F, E AND G

2

INDIAN DANCE

Slowly   American

3

mp

AMERICAN FOLK TUNE

Moderato

4

FOR SMOOTH FINGERS

Seconds

5

Play for smooth fingers - then for speed!

JADE WINGS

Ed Sueta

Slowly

MISS MACIE

Ed Sueta

Lively

TWO PART CANON

English

Recorder 1 starts at the beginning. When Recorder 1 reaches, Recorder 2 starts at the beginning.

D

Low D is a space note.

LOW F, E AND D

HAPPY TUNE

Moderato

Ed Sueta

CHIMES

⌢• = Fermata - hold a little longer

THE SAINTS

Moderato

Traditional

mf

GOOD KING WENCESLAS

sharp

Traditional

This **sharp,** when placed here, is for all the F's in the song. This is called a **key signature**.

RHYTHM CHART 5

SYMPHONY NO. 9 - EXCERPT

GIVE ME THAT OLD TIME RELIGION

OLD BRASS WAGON

Slur - tongue first note only.

> = accent - a little more air

BINGO - FUN DUET

B♭ is a line note.

B♭

1

F AND B♭

2

For all B♭'s in this line

CHALLENGE LINE

3

Seconds

Play for smooth fingers - then for speed!

LOVELY EVENING ROUND

4

MY LORD, WHAT A MORNING

Andante   Spiritual

5

mp

FOLK TUNE DUET

English

JINGLE BELLS - DUET

Pierpont

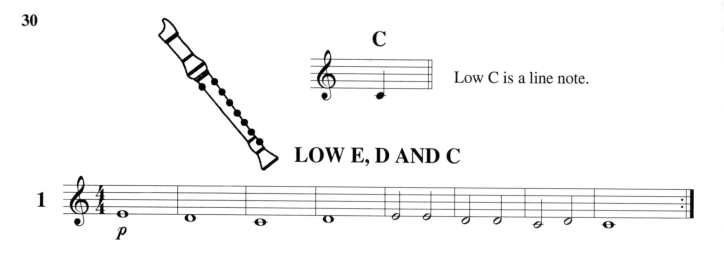

C

Low C is a line note.

LOW E, D AND C

THEME FROM THE NEW WORLD SYMPHONY

Largo = very slow

Dvorak

Fine

D.C. al Fine

GAELIC MELODY

Andante

Irish

STEAL AWAY

YANKEE DOODLE

AMERICA

GERMAN FINGERING CHART

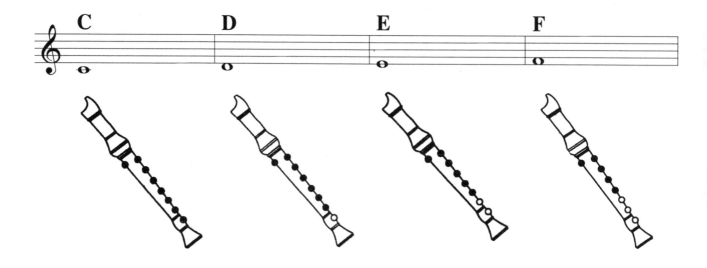

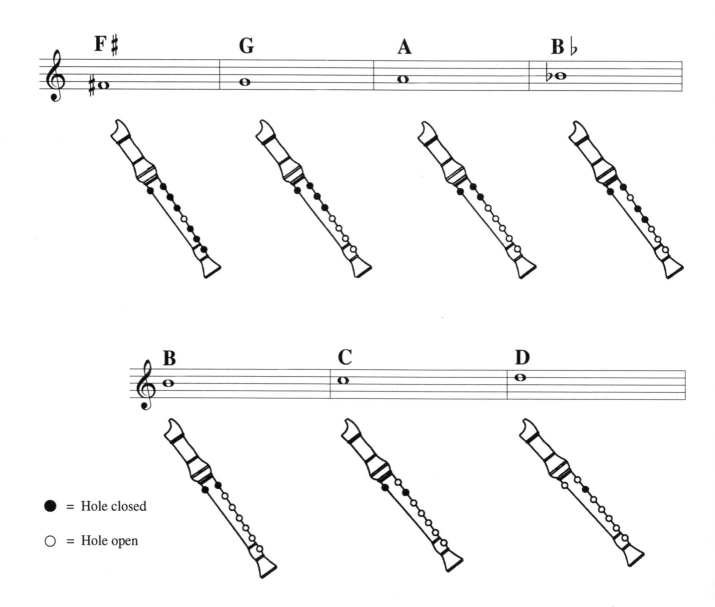

● = Hole closed

○ = Hole open